Gary Gli's Iron Shirt ProtocolsAgainst COVID-19
A Comprehensive Mind/Body Approach to Building
Super Immunity

Gary Gli

ISBN 978-0-578-72928-2

Edited by Eric J. Sobel

Cover Artwork by Edgar Brown and William Keogh

Interior Book Design by Arlene Gli

This book is dedicated to my father, John Gugliotti, who was my first and most influential teacher of Zen Mind.

FOREWORD

*L*ife in the time of COVID-19 is a new reality. New social *mores include vigilant attention to hand washing, use of antibacterial products, wearing masks and social distancing. All of these things are incredibly important, and ought to be adhered to as a matter of social responsibility. But does our responsibility end here?*

I believe what is not spoken about nearly enough concerning COVID-19, as well as the state of our health in general, is the emboldening and strengthening of our immune systems. The title of my book was inspired by the ancient art of Chinese Kung Fu, where in order to prevent the opponents' blows from damaging the inner organs, the practitioner developed what was known as an IRON SHIRT.

Each and every one of us is born with an immune system varying in strength and effectiveness. Everything from our microbiome and genome to the dietary habits of our families and more have contributed to the integrity or lack thereof concerning our unique immune systems. The good news is, regardless of the immune system we inherited, each and every one of us has been blessed with the ability and intelligence to create super immunity.

"Diet and lifestyle" has been the mantra of the conventional medical establishment for nearly 50 years, as well it should be. This campaign slogan is designed to awaken us to do our part. The holistic community goes much further in examining diet and supplementation, as well as advocating for more mind-body approaches to exercise, such as yoga, Tai Chi, pilates and most recently innovative advances in several forms of resistance training.

I subscribe to the latter, but wanted to make a case for additional simple yet highly effective mind-body practices. Moreover, what I am advocating for most strongly is a comprehensive approach. I would argue that no one modality is the golden fleece. In order to attain optimal health and well-being, it is a comprehensive endeavor. What I am offering in this book is an approach that addresses the tri-body being. What I mean by that is simply this: As human beings we are an amalgamated expression of three separate body beings -- the mental, the emotional and the physical bodies. In order to build super immunity all three bodies must be healthy and in balance with one another. It is for this reason that I often referred to the immune system as the psycho–physical immune system. If we are in emotional crisis consciously or unconsciously the biology and chemistry of the physical body will be compromised no matter how healthy our eating. Therefore, it is imperative that we address the whole body being.

In this book I will cover the practices of Conscious Consumption, Conscious Breathing, Meditation, Affirmations and Visualization. Most importantly, I will introduce and break down the guiding principle of Spiritual Science or quantum reality, which essentially *breathes life into these practices. When these practices are performed in the realization of our inseparability from Infinite Power, they hold miraculous potential.*

PREFACE

Look past your disease to the Universe. Allow the Universe to deal with it, for its intelligence is infinite!

What this book is and what it is not

What it is not:
Number one...this book is NOT intended to diagnose, treat, or cure any disease. If you have symptoms of concern seek the help of a licensed physician or other medical professional.

Number two... this book is NOT a complete and comprehensive guide to Spiritual Enlightenment. In order for such an inquiry to be optimal a much more comprehensive understanding of Spiritual Science would be required. In addition to that, several other practices would be necessary in order to fully inculcate the tenets of Spiritual Science, including an understanding and adherence to virtue as well as a code of high moral conduct.

Number three...It is NOT a complete guide to diet and nutrition. Truth be told: at this point in time if one were interested in forging and maintaining an optimal dietary plan it must be one designed on an individual basis. Furthermore, if anyone is dealing with chronic conditions or autoimmune dysfunction it would be more than prudent to seek out the guidance of a doctor of functional medicine. Examinations that include blood and microbiome testing will provide the best information necessary to create an eating plan that specifically addresses one's needs. Eating medicinally to reverse disease processes is not a one-size-fits-all approach. One man's food is another man's poison. If one cannot afford to see a functional physician at the moment or cannot afford testing, then through a process of careful elimination, one must remain attentive to which foods agree or disagree with them. Be sure to eat whole real food, but understand that not all good food will be good for you!

What this book is:

This book is a manual comprising a powerful protocol to embolden and strengthen the psycho-physical immune system and forge our IRON SHIRT. It lays out a sufficient understanding of Spiritual Science in tandem with several purposefully chosen mind/body practices that carry crossover potential from their highest ideals of enlightenment and liberation to survival of the fittest. Although we can do a bit more in terms of diet, delve more deeply into Spiritual Science and add a few more practices, that in no way undermines the power of this protocol. What

I have chosen to put forth in this work is certainly comprehensive enough and the sum is greater than its parts. The synergy of the practices that comprise this IRON SHIRT PROTOCOL will prove to be powerful beyond measure.

INTRODUCTION

"When you realize that eternity is right here now, that it is within your possibility to experience the eternity of your own truth and being, then you grasp the following: That which you are was never born and will never die." - Joseph Campbell

What is Spiritual Science and why is it included in this work?

Spiritual Science is the study of the alignment or reflection of the individual *mind* with Universal MIND. It reveals that each individual *mind* is a hologram of the *Whole* and so is identical in nature. Therefore, each individual, in essence, remains *inseparable* from the *Whole*. What this means in reality is that we have *Unlimited Universal Power* at our disposal — a crucial thing to know in order to fortify and supercharge our immunity or to recover from any disease. The practices of *conscious consumption, conscious breathing, meditation, affirmations and visualizations* serve a dual purpose. These practices serve first and foremost as a reminder of our *true identity* while at the same time providing the means to bring this *Universal Power* into manifestation. If our application of these practices is earnest, nothing we intend lives outside the *field of infinite possibilities.* Committing to these few practices in the light of *Spiritual Science* enables us to look past the world of appearance to the deeper REALITY free of *fear, guilt* and *doubt.* The knowledge that we are forever an aspect of *Infinite Intelligence* and *Power* grants us the permission to create freely and definitively. As we become even more comfortable in this knowledge we can begin to combine these *mind/body* practices in creative and seemingly endless ways. This will serve to augment our daily practice exponentially and increase its efficacy. Our *IRON SHIRT* can now be forged!

Most holistic practitioners whom you may see on YouTube or whose newsletters you may read concentrate most, if not all, of their efforts on nutrition. My contention is that nutrition, although a critical component, is only one part of a much more comprehensive program to achieve optimal physical, mental and emotional health. Moreover, the efficacy of the supplements we take and the practices we keep is directly proportionate to our *intention* to *heal.* They are mere extensions of our *mind* and MIND is all there is. In fact, to discount the *mind* in any and all substantial cases of *healing* would be willfully blind. Protocols of supplementation and practices may vary, but the common denominator in all remission and reversal is the *mind.*

In this book I have distilled and highlighted ten super-supplements and six tenets of *conscious consumption* that will prove to be most effective in dealing, not only with COVID-19 and other viruses, but also with any crises that impact the physical body. These ten super-supplements, six tenets of *conscious consumption* and the select *mind/body* practices that I have chosen to share with you, especially when used in tandem with one another and in the light of *Spiritual Science*, will provide you undoubtedly with the highest level of immune support. In my desire to serve everyone and anyone who is interested in the pursuit of supercharging their immune system, but may not be interested or able to commit fully to the more comprehensive undertaking of either *Spiritual Enlightenment* or *Optimal Health*, this book will be of immense value. The fact that this book is concise and simple to follow in no way implies it will be less effective. In the name of *healing*, supercharging your *psycho-physical* immune system, and making yourself an inhospitable host, not only in the time of COVID-19 but in order to meet all challenges that will surely be posed by new emerging pathogens, I offer you this work.

TABLE OF CONTENTS

MY JOURNEY TO SELF DISCOVERY

"No individual can ultimately fail. The Divinity which descends into humanity is bound to re-gain its original state. " - N. Sri Ram

My name is Gary Gli and I am an intuit, spiritual life coach and advisor. I founded Conscious Movement, Inc. in 1987. The mission of Conscious Movement since its inception has been to guide folks toward *clarity, liberation* and *peace*. Prior to the pandemic I had been working on a comprehensive book entitled "Ten Practices of a Spiritual Warrior," which in essence is the codification of my system of *Functional Spirituality*. When it became apparent that this emerging pandemic was inescapable, I decided it might be timely and important to distill some of the practices contained in this larger yet still unfinished work, and streamline and repackage them to be presented in this short book as a simple, effective and immediate response to COVID-19. I chose the practices that most succinctly addressed the emboldening of our *psycho-physical* immunity. I say *psycho-physical* because it is imperative that we not only bolster the immune system of the physical body to guard against pathogens but at the same time strengthen the *mind's* resolve to deal with crisis. I have been teaching these ancient and effective practices for many years in my private practice. Therefore, this book will surely outlive this crisis, and prove valuable both as an introduction to my forthcoming book as well as a guide to negotiate future events such as this one.

From a very young age I was drawn to both the martial arts and music. I was fully committed to each one of these arts, sometimes simultaneously, and at other times giving full attention to only one of them. Because they seemed to be so very different, requiring physical expressions that were antithetical to one another, I often found myself frustrated. Nonetheless, in my passion, I continued to pursue them both in spite of the tension. In the early 1970s a new TV series, *Kung Fu* starring David Carradine, was being launched. The series was aired at the exact time that I was studying Southern Praying Mantis Kung Fu in New York City's Chinatown. I was especially intrigued by the spiritual lessons portrayed in each show. They were Zen Buddhist teachings as adhered to by the monks in the Shaolin Temple. From what I learned, I began to realize that the subtext to achieving excellence in any and/or multiple endeavors was the uncovering of the *consciousness* that lived behind them. By prioritizing *consciousness* in and of itself, I witnessed my body become less dense and more malleable. I would be remiss not to mention the importance of cultivating *presence* as part of this process. Being able to now shape-shift my body, the tension between my martial art pursuits and my musical aspirations disappeared. I discovered not only harmony and liberation in universal expression, but the *Source* of *Power* that lies behind the world of forms.

Alongside these now twin endeavors I was also strength training, writing, teaching and profoundly committed to the study of Eastern Spirituality and Gnostic Christian teachings. Drawing from my experience concerning the work ethic necessary to freely create in any art, I realized the same was true concerning spiritual discovery. Moreover, as a professional teacher of several martial arts, I developed the skill to usefully break down the techniques and concepts I was hoping to transmit. This is what led me to codify my system of *Functional Spirituality*. I believe that whatever religion or brand of spirituality we subscribe to, it must serve to move us closer to the TRUTH that we are ONE with INFINITE INTELLIGENCE, aka GOD. It must include PRACTICES that function as re-minders of this TRUTH, and so allow us to draw *power, healing, unreasonable joy* and *peace* from it.

The universal birthright we all share in equally is our capacity and potential for *healing* the *whole body being*. In the name of such *healing,* supercharging your *psycho-physical* immune system and making yourself an inhospitable host to COVID-19, I will teach you the same successful practices that I have used to guide professional fighters, world-class athletes and performance artists, as well as countless lay people to discover their highest potential.

Fear can sometimes be a great motivator. Couple that fear

with the new reality of social distancing, while so much uncertainty prevails, and we as humans begin to seek out ways both to empower ourselves and find *peace of mind.* Without being able to engage the social distractions we normally use to ignore our deeply buried feelings of discomfort in the form of *inadequacy, self-doubt* and *angst,* we are willing to lend an ear. Again, because of the immediate nature of this crisis and my desire to include anyone and everyone, I decided to keep the protocol in this book limited and easy to use. No prior knowledge or experience is necessary. Some of you may choose to delve deeper into nutrition and practices such as these on your own. Let me say that I wholeheartedly encourage you to do so. The deeper you dig the greater the treasure. The most important piece of advice that I can offer is that whatever bona fide information you garner and take onboard, you extend *faith* in such while remaining consistent and persistent in your pursuit.

THE SOURCE OF OUR POWER

"When we argue for our limitations we get to keep them." - Evelyn Waugh

J esus said "Ye shall KNOW the TRUTH and the TRUTH shall set ye free." The TRUTH that Jesus alludes to is this: We arise into the world of form out of the formless, omnipresent and omnipotent field of INFINITE INTELLIGENCE, aka GOD, are sustained by it throughout our life here, and fall back into it when we leave our bodies behind. Because we become mesmerized by form (the narcissistic complex) the TRUTH of *inseparability* remains obscured. Hence, we are deluded into believing we are finite alien creatures in a dead hostile universe and so are powerless. In our desperation and in order to find solace we may rely on what is familiar and create God in our image and likeness. We may then petition Him or Her in prayer to intervene and save us. This false belief of limitation is self-imposed, and so can be undone through the *recognition* of *inseparability. Recognition*, however, means to KNOW once again. The TRUTH Jesus speaks of is no more than a comforting idea unless we come to KNOW it. Knowing it is

5

far different from knowing *about* it. Remember, God helps those who help themselves! The few practices I have included in this book are a means to helping ourselves KNOW and when we know we are *inseparable* from *God* we are *liberated*. *Liberated* from what you may ask? *Liberated* from the world of form and the bylaws that govern it.

That is why Jesus also reminds us to be in the world, not of it. When we realize that the root of our being lies in the realm of the *Unmanifested*, or the *Kingdom of Heaven*, all things are possible. Realizing the illusory nature of the world, including our own *mind/body matrix*, we know it is malleable, and can and will be shaped by unyielding and committed *intention*. Quantum mechanics has long validated the phenomenon that mere observation influences the sub-atomic universe, transforming waves into particles. As you may already know, the world of form is comprised of particles. To date these particles prove to be ninety-nine and nine-tenths percent empty space. As microscopes and other instruments become more advanced we may learn what Yogis and Spiritual Avatars have been claiming for millennia, that all is comprised of light flashing in and out so quickly we cannot see or measure it. This begs the questions: where does this light come from and where does it go when it disappears? Does it simply cross the thin line between the *unmanifested* and the world of form? Does anything material really exist? If mere observation brings things into existence, what might observation coupled with *intention* bring into existence? This is the stuff of miracles.

There are three important things to know here:

1) The practices laid out here, including *conscious consumption* in the form of nutrition, are both a means toward the TRUTH as well as an expression of it.

2) The world of form is governed by the ego or carnal mind, and so inadvertently and/or deliberately blocks our advancement toward *liberation*. It inherently possesses a tow similar to the ocean, and so these practices are an anchor.

3) Last, but most importantly, it is not a zero-sum game! To completely and unequivocally KNOW the TRUTH would portend perfection. We all understand that perfection is not possible. So now what? If I don't KNOW the truth how will it set me free? Good question! Well, we have all heard it said that *God* is *Love* or that the *Universe* rises up to meet us half way. The nature of *Love* is to serve. Whenever we make a sincere effort we invite the *forgiving nature* of the *Universe* to enter. Our desire and efforts to embody the TRUTH, although not fully possible, still moves the needle substantially closer to it.

If a prize fighter or musician earnestly, consistently and persistently pursues excellence or perfection, though they may never achieve their ideal, the level they are capable of attaining is monumental. We have all witnessed victories in sporting events that we describe as miraculous. How against all odds and in spite of rationale the *spirit* of the underdog prevails.

Developing *Iron Shirt Immunity* or facilitating spontaneous remission is more common than we hear of because the world of perceived limitation has a vested interest in telling us otherwise. At the end of the day only you can decide whether or not you will extend *faith* along with a committed work ethic to achieve the goal of super immunity.

CREATING OUR IRON SHIRT

"First, learn to become invincible, then wait for your enemy's moment of vulnerability." – Sun Tzu

When boxers or mixed martial artists step into the ring or octagon, they have prepared rigorously to build a defense that does not allow them to be hit. They know full-well, however, that that is not fully possible. If they are in such an arena, they most certainly are going to be hit. Therefore, they spend a considerable amount of their training conditioning their bodies so that they are capable of taking blows that their defense was incapable of stopping. In the Chinese art of Kung Fu, they take this understanding to a much deeper and more comprehensive level known as *IRON SHIRT*. It is a practice whereby the body is locked down in such a way that the musculoskeletal system integrates and repels the blows, not allowing them to permeate this created shell and harm the inner organs. At the same time, the inner organs compress and yield deep into the subtle body so that they are malleable and indestructible. In the same way, no matter how many times we wash our hands, wear gloves, or are mindful, there are going to be times we are inadvertently exposed. The question now becomes can the virus be killed on contact, or, if it should enter the body, can it be dealt with and mitigated before it permeates deeper into the lungs? The answer is a resounding yes.

In mounting our defense against invading pathogens we must begin systemically. Power always emanates from the center outward. This is why the *mind* as profiled in *Spiritual Science* is paramount. It is for all intents and purposes the center of our *mind/body* matrix. Let's look at a useful metaphor to better help us understand the efficacy in layering.

During medieval times if an invading army were out to kill the king they would have to storm his castle. The castle itself was the strongest line of defense. It represents the center. It was built purposefully with a deep foundation as well as thick and high walls. As the invading army encroached they would have to deal with the arrows of the archers who were strategically perched at the top of the castle walls and perhaps a brigade of knights on horseback going out to do battle. The objective was always to stop the onslaught furthest in proximity from the king (Not unlike our own immune systems.) If the invading army managed to get past the knights and the archers, however, they would come upon a moat filled with alligators. If they negotiated the moat they would have to bring down the draw bridge and break through a thick bolted door, all while being pelted from the soldiers at the top of the castle. Once they entered they would have to confront the foot soldiers. Should they have gotten closer to the king, he would be defended by his vassals. Our immune systems are akin to this metaphor of the castle. Our mindset, one that *refuses* to be ill, is the castle itself. Depending on how deep our *conviction*, the thicker and higher the walls. Denying entry is the objective. If for whatever reason this proves to not be the case our army is ready and able.

The king's army, which used arrows, swords, spears, axes and daggers, is similar to our collective immune system, using the microbiome (not only in our gut but on our skin), white blood cells, phagocytes and lymphocytes. Pathogens must burrow through many layers of defense before compromising our immunity. Realizing just how intelligent and complex the immune system is, and understanding just how robust we can make it, should in itself instill confidence and bring us a measure of comfort. Each human being is fully equipped to deal with invasion from pathogens and microbes. Washing our hands, wearing masks and maintaining social distancing is akin to the arrows shot from the top of the castle. More often than not, battles would ensue closer to the castle, if not within its walls. We must invest in the castle itself first and foremost. Like a king who trusts his castle, knights, and vassals we too must trust our *Innate Intelligence*, supplementation and the *mind/body* practices laid out in this work

In studying people who have cured themselves of so-called "incurable diseases" and have experienced what is known as a radical remission, we come to see that the common denominator is an *unflinching state of mind* that *refuses* to be sick. This ZEN MIND sees itself as *already* healed.

Investing in and upholding this state of mind, above and beyond all doubt, is the challenge. Our sword of virtue must be held high. Alongside *faith*, it will call for *courage* and *acceptance* in equal measure to put a stake in the ground while understanding a fair amount of random expressions do exist in this universe, and so our intentions may not always come to fruition.

Because of the inherent duality of this temporal plane we must strike a balance between opposing realities that are yet to be made manifest. We must plan as though we are going to live forever, but live as though we are going to die tomorrow. The following story illustrates this point beautifully.

Joe Louis, the great boxing champion of the 1930s and 40s, who said he would never lose, was interviewed many years after he retired. Sports writers asked him: Joe, did you really think you would never lose? After a long pause he chuckled and said, "Of course not, we all have to lose, but not on that night and not to that bum." What this illustrates is that in order to be a great champion, although losing is always a possibility, the champion in that moment does not have the luxury to acknowledge defeat. He must commit to not allowing that possibility into existence.

Again, it takes great *courage* to refuse to accept no alternative outcome to our vision and great *fortitude* in maintaining *vigilance* toward bringing our vision to fruition. More specifically, this *vigilance* must remain single-pointed toward the ego which can and will hijack our ability to commit with such authority. It will sabotage our efforts by sowing *doubt.* But if we recognize that what we're hoping to bring into existence is actually an *extension* of what has *already* been created we draw the cards of *trust* and *humility* and release all tension. We recognize that although we as seemingly separate individuals are not capable of such grandiosity, by realigning with creation, a function of the *mind/body* practices, our *power* is immense. With every supplement and breath we take, with every *affirmation* and *visualization* we make, we will feel a tightening of the fabric that holds the iron in place. One practice supports the other. We will experience this collective protocol as a living amalgam that synergistically fortifies itself.

Now of course, as Joe Louis understood, we are not invincible. This is important to understand because should the first line of defense be breached or perhaps the first few lines, the ego will take advantage of this lull and pile on. We cannot run the risk of becoming demoralized and so we must, against all head winds, maintain *trust* and *fortitude.*

It would be a huge oversight not to bring the following clarification to light. The primordial and MOST effective way to build our *IRON SHIRT* is our interaction with microbes.

13

The most recent understanding concerning our mutual coexistence with bacteria, viruses and fungi has led pioneers in the field of epigenetics to redefine humans as super-organisms. Under normal circumstances we should not fear our relationship with microbes but seek to live in harmony with them. Just as that boxer or mixed martial artist I mentioned at the beginning of this chapter MUST spar with his partners to prepare himself for combat we MUST sharpen our immune system by interacting with bugs.

Babies and toddlers put anything and everything into their mouths instinctually so their bodies can decipher information to help build the immune system. Tonsils are actually a learning device that compiles information from microbes entering the body through the mouth. Constantly misusing anti bacterial products destroys the micro biome on the skin which is our first line of defense. Having said that, there are exceptions to every rule. Due to the highly contagious nature of COVID-19 now, and perhaps newer and more deadly pathogens emerging in the future, what might normally be considered obsessive may turn out to be prudent. In the same way you might now, in light of the information I just shared, not become alarmed watching a toddler put their foot in their mouth, you most certainly at the same time would not encourage them to eat lead. We must learn to think on our feet lest we are bound by a defunct plan. Being ideologically driven at the expense of critical thinking and mental/emotional flexibility can get us killed!

During a highly contagious pandemic such as COVID-19, proper hygiene such as hand washing, face masks and social distancing actually help a population develop herd immunity. How? Just as the defenders inside the castle would breathe a sigh of relief if the invading army was smaller than their own, our immune systems breathe a sigh of relief when the viral load is lower. If the immune system is not overwhelmed by too large a dose of the virus it can more easily begin to make antibodies. Practicing the appropriate external protocols limits our exposure, making it less likely that our castle will be overrun.

Gary Gli

CONSCIOUS CONSUMPTION

"Let food be thy medicine and medicine be thy food." - Hippocrates

As I mentioned in the introduction, it is not my intention to provide an expansive and comprehensive nutritional protocol, as that could be an entire book in and of itself. I might also add that *conscious consumption* in its highest ideal is a commitment that I cannot assume you are willing to make. However, in order to maintain the integrity of this work and fulfill its promise as a guide to supercharge our immune systems, I must include a few common denominators concerning *conscious consumption* where a broad consensus has been reached. I would also be remiss not to mention the fact that our immune systems will be severely compromised if they are overburdened with toxins. Before we can build and fortify our immune system we must first detoxify. Again, the most effective way to ensure we are not only detoxifying but also not adding more toxins generated from the foods we believe to be good for us but may not be, testing is required. A detailed approach aimed solely at detoxification is a bit complex, and so not included in this work. I recommend that you research the many protocols that are designed to accomplish that end. The following is a broad guideline to eating well and gently clearing out some of the toxic build up:

Eliminate sugar, dairy and all processed foods, including white breads, while eating organic, unprocessed whole food. Eating sugary foods and desserts along with processed foods will create fermentation in the gut. This will compromise the lining of the intestines, causing toxic waste to flood the bloodstream. This intestinal permeability is known as leaky gut syndrome, and is the impetus to most autoimmune dysfunction. Moreover, this fermentation, along with the pesticides found in inorganic fruit, vegetables, farmed fish and meats, will disrupt the microbiome, which, again, is the seat of our *psycho-physical* immune system. Generally speaking, eating whole real food will ensure nutritional density and prevent further toxification of the body.

Once again you may have noticed I used the term *psycho-physical* immune system, and in this case it is to make the express point that the disposition of our microbiome directly affects our moods and overall mental health. In order for us to be fully *present* to the other practices included in this work, our physical chemistry must comply. If we are overburdened with cortisol, for example, we will have trouble focusing and maintaining *presence* when engaging these other practices.

This can also be an opportune time to begin a practice of

intermittent fasting for at least two days a week. Intermittent fasting is eating within a six to eight hour window and drinking only water for the next eighteen to sixteen hours, respectively. It has been shown that doing this for only two days a week without even changing one's diet profoundly influences our blood profile markers positively. If one were in good health and in communication with a doctor or health care professional I would also encourage a three-day water fast to optimally impact our blood profile.

Regardless of how much of the aforementioned we take onboard, I strongly suggest that we educate ourselves about the many ways we can eat to achieve optimal health and well-being. For now, by trusting our intuition and feeling what speaks to us, we will be able to modify and create a diet and supplementation plan that is balanced and prudent.

I would like to spend a brief moment discussing the concept of medicinal eating and supplementation. In folklore, we often see certain foods as healing. Chicken soup, for example, comes to mind. For many of my Jewish friends this will ring true. For the common cold or flu, a fresh bowl of "made with love" chicken soup is the answer. This is just one example, as each culture will tout its unique foods, herbs and spices carefully prepared in secret family recipes for mending. Now it's not as though we could not enjoy a bowl of chicken soup just because, but it takes on a medicinal quality when feeling ill. Because this tasty and soothing remedy will hold an *intention* of *healing* a vibration of *Love* will be transmitted. Understanding quantum reality we could make the case that the soup is merely the conduit of *Love*, which in essence is what is ultimately responsible for *healing* us, but that's for another book. The take-away is that we should choose, prepare and eat our food with the *intention* to embolden our immune systems.

I would also like to bring to light the time-sensitive component to self-healing. As we cultivate the ability to become more *present* through the *mind/body* practices in this book, most especially *meditation*, we will also become aware of all that enters our space immediately. This is incredibly useful when sensitizing our body awareness to the very beginning of an illness process. In the same way that the archers and knights sought to thwart an attack outside the walls of the castle, when we begin medicinal supplementation at the beginning of any disease process, we have a greater chance of thwarting it. During a pandemic such as COVID-19, where a pervasive and highly contagious virus is in play, I for the most part recommend a more generic, medicinal approach as a prophylactic. Again, I strongly suggest that you research further concerning these supplements, and perhaps in time cut back on some of them or temporarily discontinue their use. Taking a break from using some of these supplements will actually increase their efficacy when reintroduced.

Six common denominators and tenets of conscious consumption:
1) Drink a minimum of 8 to 10 8oz glasses of natural spring

water or properly filtered water a day. A pinch of pink Himalayan salt in a few of those glasses will maintain your electrolytes, enabling better tissue hydration.

2) Avoid or minimize sugar/sweets and table salt.

3) Follow a plant-based whole food diet with adequate fiber. No processed foods!

4) Buy certified organic foods. Concerning fruits and vegetables this is especially important when the skin or outer layer is thin and/or porous. Google the "dirty dozen" and the "clean fifteen."

5) Avoid fried foods.

6) Eat your last meal or snack at least 3 hours before sleeping.

Here is a list of simple and easy to use supplements to bolster the immune system against viruses in general, and from what we know presently, COVID-19 as well. If possible, I would suggest using the first 3 supplements in the following order upon waking. Numbers 4 through 8 should be taken after breakfast or another meal. The probiotics should be taken one half hour before lunch or dinner and Manuka honey at your discretion.

1. **Bragg's Organic Raw - Unfiltered and Unpasteurized Apple Cider Vinegar with the Mother**: One tablespoon in warm water to start your day is sufficient. Any other brand of the same quality is acceptable. You can occasionally substitute this product with one half organic lemon in warm water. Because of the acidity, a useful tip would be to rinse one's mouth with warm water after this step.

2. 8 ounces of fresh green juice and perhaps another 8 ounces later in the day. If making fresh juice is not possible, there are some wonderful over-the-counter green powders that are highly effective. Personally, I have been using *Green Vibrance* for over twenty years. By all means, you can use any green powder product that is highly rated and fits your budget. No need to stop using these foods.

3. Oreganol: I regularly follow the prescribed dosage of 2 drops under the tongue daily. During the COVID-19 crisis I increased the dosage to four drops under the tongue daily. You can occasionally discontinue using this product for several weeks to a month before reintroducing.

4. Liposomal vitamin C: As a prophylactic or maintenance dose I take 1 to 3 g daily, spread out throughout the day. At the onset of feeling ill or if I feel as though I've been exposed during the typical flu season or a pandemic such as this one I may increase my intake from 6 to 10 g, again spread out throughout the day. Bowel intolerance is a reliable indicator that one may have taken too much. In that case, one can cut back 1 g at a time until bowel tolerance is reestablished. No need to stop vitamin C supplementation.

5. Vitamin D3: Personally, I take from 2000 to 5000IU. When taking a vitamin D supplement, it is imperative to take vitamin K2 as well. There are some really good supplements that include calcium and vitamin K2. These three work synergistically to ensure proper absorption and assimilation of calcium. Vitamin K2 is important when using vitamin D and calcium, as it directs the calcium to the bone matrix as opposed to the bloodstream, where too much calcium can cause arterial calcification. In terms of fighting viruses, vitamin K2 and calcium are not really necessary, but a product such as this gives you more bang for your buck. Spending 20 minutes before noon or after 3 PM absorbing the sun's rays over as much unclothed skin as possible helps the body manufacture the highest quality vitamin D money can't buy. I usually take 5000 IU during the winter months when it is not possible to get sufficient sun exposure. During the summer months I may drop to 2000 IU per day.

6. Curcumin: This is the active ingredient in turmeric and is an incredibly medicinal spice. It has amazing anti-inflammatory and cancer fighting properties. It also is a very powerful agent against viral attack, and bolsters the immune system. You can also feel free to cook with organic turmeric. I myself regularly take 500 mg of curcumin per day. You can occasionally discontinue using cur cumin for up to a week.

7. Zinc: 8 - 11 mg of zinc a day is recommended for most adults. More than 40 mg is too much. You can use zinc supplements or if you prefer to get your zinc from foods, the following food are rich in zinc:
a. Red meat
b. Poultry
c. Beans
d. Nuts and seeds
e. Whole grains

I do not recommend getting zinc through dairy products, as dairy can be inflammatory. There is competing data as to whether zinc acetate or zinc gluconate works better against a common cold. I have used both with much success. The problem with zinc is getting it deep enough into the cells, especially when dealing with coronaviruses.

8. Quercetin: This antiviral is not only effective in supporting healthy lung function, which is of monumental importance when dealing with a respiratory virus such as COVID-19, but more importantly is responsible for driving zinc deep into each cell. Getting the zinc into the cell is important to help kill the virus. The synergistic effect of zinc with quercetin creates a powerful homeopathic remedy. I take 500 mg after breakfast and after dinner as well. You can occasionally take a short break from taking this supplement. If you prefer to get your daily quercetin through food rather than supplementation, you can load up on onions in your daily meals or try making this tea:

a. Boil water. Then add orange peels, onion skins, ginger & rosemary twigs.

b. Turn down heat, cover and simmer for 20 minutes.

c. Strain and drink throughout the day.

9. Probiotics: The microbiome or our intestinal gut flora is the seat of our immune system. It is also considered a second brain as there are more neurotransmitters in the gut than in the brain. Our disposition and mood are greatly affected by the ratio of good-to-bad bacteria in the microbiome.

Therefore, regular use of a good and high-quality probiotic is advisable about one half hour before dinner. If you prefer to get your probiotics from food, I suggest kimchi first and foremost. Of course, yogurt and kefir are known sources of probiotics, but I personally avoid these as dairy can be inflammatory. I do know that there is a consensus that both yogurt and kefir made from goats' milk is preferable. Whichever choices you decide on, it is crucial and important that you pay attention to the microbiome through regularly ingesting probiotics. No need to discontinue.

10. Manuka honey with an MGO of 250+: Especially in dealing with COVID-19, a dollop on the tongue allowed to slowly coat your throat is advisable, as this grade of honey has many antiviral and antibacterial qualities. I use Manuka honey medicinally, not on a regular basis.

Choosing the term *conscious consumption* was very purposeful on my part. We often think of diet as food or substances that we take into our physical bodies, absorbing what is useful and eliminating what is not. But this does not take into account the mental and emotional bodies that comprise the human matrix along with the physical body. In the same way that we need to be mindful of what we put into our bodies to ensure proper nutrition and not overburden them with toxins, we must be mindful of what we ingest in the form of *thoughts, beliefs* and other external stimuli.

Unfortunately, we have already inherited thoughts and

beliefs courtesy of our genome that comprises the critical mass of our overarching thought-construct. Moreover, from in-vitro through early childhood and on, many other limiting thoughts and beliefs have been further ingrained into our psyche through familial and societal indoctrination. Just as the physical body needs to be detoxified before we can rebuild, the same is true of the mental and emotional bodies. This is why the study of *Spiritual Science* is important. *Spiritual Science* enlightens us to the TRUTH which lives above and beyond acquired thoughts and beliefs. On a mental and emotional level it provides psychic nutrition in the form of *inspired* and *redeemed* thinking while simultaneously detoxifying by evaporating old conditioning. Once we have reasonably enlightened our minds, the *thoughts* and *beliefs* we must now subscribe to need to be in line with TRUTH. Our compass is *principle* and *virtue*, which when adhered to, ensures that this alignment remains integral.

BONUS MATERIAL

The importance of maintaining adequate oxygen levels in the blood and tissues is essential to good health. Oxygen is a fundamental element needed to bolster our immune system. Obviously, exercise and conscious breathing will elevate our oxygen levels, but in terms of diet, antioxidant rich foods such as berries, beans and raw greens, along with an array of supplements like CoQ10(ubiquinol), Alpha Lipoic acid and vitamin C, will aid in oxygen uptake. Here is a bonus I am adding to conscious consumption because although it is not taken orally we do ingest through the skin.

Peroxide Foot Soak......a simple and highly effective oxygen therapy:

Ingredients:
1) Water: 50 parts
2) Hydrogen peroxide 3%: 1 Part
3) Epsom salt: 1 teaspoon

Fill a basin with very warm water so that it covers the feet up to the ankles. Add 3 ounces of hydrogen peroxide 3% and a teaspoon of Epsom salt. Soak feet for 20 minutes. Hydrogen peroxide H202 is similar to water H2O but as you can see has an additional oxygen molecules. When hydrogen peroxide is dispersed in water, it decomposes. Epsom salt, which is comprised of magnesium, sulfur and oxygen, also contributes to this decomposition. We are now soaking our feet in an oxygen rich solution. It is believed in the fields of holistic and alternative medicine that the soles of the feet are key absorption points.

Gary Gli

CONSCIOUS BREATHING

*"There is one way of breathing that is shameful and constricted.
Then, there's another way: a breath of love that takes you all the
way to infinity." - Rumi*

Conscious breathing is a form of *meditation*, but remains a practice in and of itself. By simply focusing our attention on feeling the breath rise and fall we inadvertently quiet the *mind* and interrupt our habitual, and sometimes debilitating, thinking patterns. If one were to have a lot on their mind but then a heavy object fell on their toe, you can rest assured that, at least temporarily, whatever was on their mind would be completely blotted out by the pain in their toe. The more profoundly you *feel* the breath, the more *still* the *mind*. This lapse in thinking is why we can call conscious breathwork a form of *meditation*.

Breathing slowly into the diaphragm or what Taoists and other masters of eastern mysticism might refer to as the primordial chakra or dantian (energy center), has its own benefits. As this energy center is awakened, the flow of internal energy in the body, or the chi, begins to circulate unencumbered, bathing and renewing our organ systems. It is important to remember that we are energy systems at the behest of our *Innate Intelligence*, and so our energetic resonance precedes our biology and gross physicality. By becoming aware of and identifying with the energy flow in the body, we return to the primordial bridge of our creation, and so are renewed. Our immune system is emboldened, our endocrine system is recalibrated, and our blood pressure and anxiety levels are lowered.

All of the breathing patterns I have carefully chosen to share with you in this work will relax the *mind* and body, mitigating negative stress. Each one of them, however, will address and prioritize slightly different affects upon the body.

The ability to understand, establish and maintain neutral spine is most important when utilizing these breathing concepts while sitting, standing or walking. Neutral spine is the back bone of perfect posture. When perfect posture is established and the alignment is correct, signals from the brain through the brainstem are able to travel down the spine and through the associated nerves, sending electromagnetic signals to the organ systems keeping them integral. When doing the breathing exercises in a supine position, a soft adherence to neutral spine is all that is required, whereas when sitting, standing and/or walking we must apply appropriate tension to keep the core of the body taut yet elastic.

Establishing Neutral Spine:

1) We lie on our backs with our feet flat on the floor and knees sharply bent toward the ceiling.

2) We gently retract our chins toward the back of our necks or the floor.

3) We keep our buttocks on the ground while pinching our shoulder blades together and keep them pinned to the ground.

4) We establish a full arch in the lower back by pushing our bellies as high up toward the ceiling as we can. (We should be able to easily place our hands under our lower backs.)

5) Now we slowly flatten our lower backs to the floor then back up to the top in a full arch. We continue to do this several times until we can sense the distance from the flattened position to the full arch.

6) While continuing this movement we notice the half-way mark (we do not pause but simply notice).

7) Now we begin to notice the quarter markers (a quarter of the way down, half-way down, three-quarters of the way down, flat / a quarter of the way up, half-way up, three-quarters of the way up, full arch), and when we are confident that we have a reasonably good sense of the markers we STOP!

8) We return to full arch and come down 20% to 25% and lock it in.

We make sure the chin is retracted toward the back of the neck (this is crucial to allow the spine to fully open and stretch).

THIS IS OUR NEUTRAL SPINE POSITION

Exercise 1 (Belly Breathing):

1) Lying on our backs with our feet flat on the floor and knees sharply bent toward the ceiling, we gently retract our chins toward the back of our necks or the floor.

2) For this exercise our backs remains flat on the floor (it is NOT a neutral spine position).

3) Gently isolate the dantian which is located two inches below the navel, and place the center of a book directly over it. We breathe in through the nose for 4 counts, moving the book up toward the ceiling. Keep each breath whole and round equaling one quarter. Take care that only the belly rises, not our chest or shoulders. The breath must manifest under the book on the very first count of the inhalation. On the fourth count of the inhalation the belly should be fully distended.

4) Now we shift our attention to the book falling toward the floor, gently pushing the air out of the mouth in 25% increments.

KEEP THE BREATHING SMOOTH AND THE COUNTS WHOLE

Remember, the book is a temporary prop to help us isolate and feel the dantian as the focal point. It also helps us to understand that the breath in essence is what lifts the book. The book simply rides the wave of our inhalation and serves as an external weight that couples with gravity falling downward toward the ground through the dantian on the exhalation. In time we will be able to feel and activate the dantian without the book and in seated and standing positions as well.

This breath work will activate the dantian, and awaken the internal energy or chi. The more we relax and release tension with each inhalation, the more freely the chi will flow.

It is helpful to count in order to keep each increment of one quarter or twenty-five percent whole and even throughout the exercise. Rather than simply counting numbers we can ascribe a word to each count that functions as an auto suggestion. It may look as follows:

1) Breathe in   2) round   3) full   4) and whole

1) Out   2) relax 3) surrender 4) let go

Exercise 2 (Tailbone Breathing):

1) We establish a Soft Neutral Spine by lying on our backs with our feet extended out in front of us. Keep the knees slightly bent. We can choose to put a pillow or foam roller under our knees to support the position. Just notice and feel the natural curve that forms in the lower back. Be sure once again to retract the chin toward the back of the neck or floor.

2) We breathe in through our nose for 4 counts manifesting first in the belly then downward threading the spine to the lower back and tailbone.

3) We now breathe out of our mouths for 8 counts (each 1/8) We do not change the disposition of the spine. Imagine the flesh of the belly, sides of our waists and lower backs deflating and collapsing inward toward our neutral spine like cellophane.

4) Once the air has left our bodies, we pause and hold with our lungs empty for 4 counts until we begin the next inhalation. Now we begin to breathe in again for 4 counts. Watch and regulate that first inhalation making sure it is precisely 25%. After exhaling for 8 counts and remaining without air in the lungs for 4 counts, the natural proclivity is to gasp. This is what makes the first inhalation of the next cycle so sacred. I myself always strive to enter here at slightly less than 25%, perhaps closer to 22%-23%.

This seemingly minor act of control is what will nudge us past the human condition and into our human potential. There are no small actions when intention is great. By overriding the reptilian brain's instinct to continuously breath in the name of survival, we evoke a panic response. Couple this with additional hardwiring from our ancestors who lived in an age when humans were preyed upon, and we uncover a baseline state of anxiety. This is ubiquitous in the human condition. Therefore, holding the line on the first inhalation is what most profoundly mitigates this low grade anxiety. We can also extend the count with empty lungs to challenge ourselves.

Occasionally or as an alternative, we can breathe out of the nose for eight counts while humming. A light tingling can be felt in the lips. This adjustment will allow the release of nitrous oxide stored in the nasal passages and sinuses to empty into the lungs, widening their vessels, thereby allowing oxygen to enter the circulatory system.

A SINGLE BREATH

This particular breathing pattern, because of its configuration, lends itself to a higher ideal. Of course, for each breathing pattern as well as every one of the practices in this book, *presence* is essential. I do, however, use this particular breathing pattern to pay special attention to each individual cycle and more specifically to each breath. It is always in the back of my mind that in crises, I may need to call upon one single breath to serve the purpose of centering me and allowing me access to *Infinite Power*. There may not be time for more than one. This singularity or Zen mind speaks to the sacredness of the training. We should be able to gather ourselves with a single breath.

Exercise 3 (Polarity Breathing):
1) Lying on our backs with our feet flat on the floor and our knees sharply bent towards the ceiling, we gently retract our chins toward the back of our necks or the floor.
2) We breathe in through our nose for 4 counts manifesting first in the belly then upward and into the chest. Imagine our torsos as canisters being filled from the bottom up.
3) We hold our breath for 16 counts.
4) We breathe out of our mouths or nose for 8 counts (once again keeping each increment whole and round).

The formula here is very specific: Whatever count we choose to inhale for, we will exhale for twice that number and hold for twice as long as we exhale, i.e., breathe in for 6, hold for 24, breathe out for 12. This breathing pattern helps to match our inner electro-magnetic current with the current of whatever environment we are in, reducing environmental stress. It also promotes deep cellular detoxification by elevating internal cellular pressure while flushing through sustained release.

Exercise 4 Power Breathing (Wim Hof Approach):
When doing this breathing exercise we can inhale through the mouth or the nose or both. We can be creative, in fact, and mix and match. The idea is to breathe in deeply but exhale minimally in order to fully oxygenate. We keep the accent on the inhalation bringing in more and more air. We breathe in fully, then just let it go. We breathe in deeply, then softly let go. We repeat this pattern for 30 repetitions. On the 30th repetition we expel all the air from our lungs, and remain free of air for as long as we can. Then we breathe in deeply and hold our breath for 15 seconds before letting it go.This constitutes 1 round. We repeat 2 more times to complete 3 rounds.

The Wim Hof Approach is a controlled hyperventilation or power breathing. We are creatures of adaptation, and so by inducing a voluntary and temporary stress response we mindfully push past the boundaries of the systems we are targeting. As these individual systems become more robust we ultimately enhance our overall vigor.

By rigorously breathing in we are taking up oxygen but not necessarily raising the saturation level in the blood as much as releasing a lot of carbon dioxide. It is important to keep the body relaxed and elastic so that there is no resistance and the lungs open easily. By deep breathing, we are converting the pH value in the blood to alkaline as the acidity lessens. During this phase, muscle excitability may occur as we are lowering the available calcium ions in the blood. This would account for the tingling sensation we experience in the limbs. Because the blood is now alkaline, the hemoglobin has a difficult time releasing the oxygen to the tissues. We are now in a temporary state of hypoxia. Hypoxia, when involuntary and chronic, is a serious condition whereby there is a deficiency in the amount of oxygen that reaches the tissues. Again, this is a temporary therapeutic state that we are inducing. It is a positive stress that strengthens the system, much like the controlled tearing of muscle fibers in resistance training.

When we hold the long count with no breath in the lungs the acidity level of the blood goes up. This rise in acidity is what allows the red blood cells to release their payload of oxygen to the tissues. The fact that we have lowered our levels of carbon dioxide allows us to maintain this state of transference of oxygen from the blood to the tissues for a longer period of time. The blood saturation level is now lowered significantly. This mild form of hypoxia is stressing the body at a cellular level, as the cells are not getting the normal levels of oxygen they are accustomed to. Their metabolism begins to shift, and this will signal the body to react and strengthen. The sympathetic responses are also activated, and the pathways necessary to deliver that oxygen are strengthened. There is now an increase of red blood cells, an increase in lung capacity, improved circulation and improved metabolic efficiency over the long term.

Wim Hof's Approach has also proven to increase the level of adrenaline in the blood. The levels can get so high that it becomes apparent we have influenced the sympathetic response. Further testing has proven that Wim and his students have voluntarily influenced their autonomic nervous systems as well. This was not thought possible before Wim Hof introduced his method. Through this process the immune system is profoundly emboldened and the endocrine system is recalibrated.

ALL OF THE ABOVE BREATHING PATTERNS CAN BE DONE LYING DOWN, SEATED OR STANDING

MEDITATION

"Silence is essential. We need silence just as much as we need air. If our minds are crowded with words and thoughts, there is no space for us." -
Thich Nhat Hanh

Before we move on to examine *meditation*, there are a two important points I would like to bring to light. First and more importantly, there is no such thing as a bad *meditation*. The last thing we want to do is corrupt our *meditation* practice with judgment. As a novice, each time we meditate it will prove to be a different experience. As we become more adept our experience will be less differentiated and more consistent. We must be gentle with ourselves and enjoy the process.

Secondly, I would like to draw a distinction between *meditation* and meditative concepts. From a conventional point of view they are often mistaken as one and the same. Using thought forms or any kind of imagery or body sensation to interrupt and/or detach us from our habitual thought patterns is considered to be a meditative concept. Practicing a musical instrument, painting or doing

Tai Chi are examples of this, and provide many of the benefits of *meditation* itself. By simply detaching from our incessant thought patterns and focusing on a task at hand we will de-stress the physical body, allowing energy to flow freely. Once returned to homeostasis, the proper functioning of the immune system will be reinstated.

As we can see, meditative concepts have great value. *Meditation* goes well beyond simply interrupting our thinking by focusing on other objects or endeavors regardless of how high-minded they may be. In its highest ideal, *meditation* is our experience of and *conscious reconnection* to *God* and the *Unmanifested,* our *Authentic Nature.* I'm sure you can appreciate the value of this in terms of its effect on our health and well-being. So, with that being said, let's take a look at a very simple and enjoyable *meditation.*

For this example we'll sit upright in a comfortable position, close our eyes and simply watch our thinking. Let's watch our thoughts as if we are watching a movie. There should be no attempt to judge them or change them but merely be entertained by them. Observe the way one thought gives way to another and then another after that. This is how human thinking unfolds—a string of incessant and repetitive thoughts. After a short while let's stop and take a breath.

Now we can return to watching our thoughts again. This time, however, after each thought arises we do not follow it to the next thought. For example, if the first thought that arises is "today is a beautiful day," and that is then followed by a second thought, "I think I'll go to the park," we simply pause after the first thought. Let's put a period at the end of that first thought the way we would put a period at the end of a sentence. We can imagine that our thoughts are unraveling on the pages of a book. Now smile and fix your gaze on the space. Hold it. The second thought will gently fade away.

After putting a period at the end of each thought, we can enjoy resting in the space before the next thought arises. As one does, and it surely will, we do not struggle with attempting to suppress it. Just welcome that next thought, and add another period. Inhabit the space fully while remaining alert. The spaces between each sentence will slowly and organically begin to grow. By maintaining a thread of practice there will eventually be a sentence at the top of the page and perhaps one near the bottom. One day we will open the book and there will be no sentences.

Let's examine how *meditation* is our experience of *God* and the *Unmanifested*:
The spaces on the page represent *awareness* and/or *consciousness* and all three are one and the same. It is from this *awareness* that we watch our thoughts arise. At first it appears that we are both the thinker of our thoughts and the observer of our thinking. But only one is real. All thinking is born of past and future, which have no reality. We cannot change the past, as it is but a memory trace, and the future

has yet to come. Only the present moment is real, and it is inextricably linked to our immutable state of *awareness*. Therefore, we ARE *awareness* itself first and foremost, prior, present and future to all arising thoughts and events, including our own birth. *Awareness* arises from *Infinite Intelligence* or *Life Itself* in the same way steam rises off of boiling water. This revelation once again confirms the TRUTH of our *inseparability*. As such, we are *liberated* not only from our repetitive, negative and stressful thinking, but the world itself. We are in essence in the world but not of it.

Let me share a beautiful insight that will help maintain and cultivate our practice. Now, although I do not place too much importance on how long one meditates, I do value the benefit of effortlessly maintaining *stillness* for a bit. In doing so we train the mind as well as allow the physical body time to regain homeostasis. We must be careful, however, not to compete with ourselves and disturb the grace and majesty of the moment. Have you ever been so engrossed in a book or movie that you never wanted it to end? Of course, we all have. Why is that? Because it is joyful.

Holding this space of *awareness* can sometimes prove to be quite difficult and challenging to maintain because we find ourselves wrestling with a mind conditioned to think. That can kill our joyfulness for sure. We may find ourselves continually to occasionally vacillating between witnessing the thoughts and gravitating back to the space. Although this is quite natural and to be expected in a meditative practice, we may feel as though we are unconsciously relegating the space to a mere distraction from thinking.

Now for more adept meditators who may have skillfully enhanced their ability to focus, this vacillation may not occur any longer. It is also possible that their practice may be fraught with profundity, but it can still remain a loveless exercise. What is seldom mentioned is that although the space appears to be empty, it is not. The space is comprised of *Spirit, Life Itself* and *Love* in a very literal sense. Anything and anyone that ever existed still resides in this space.

As *awareness* or *consciousness* itself we are limitless and so cannot only gaze outwardly into the space toward the periphery where thoughts either arise or do not, but we can also turn our gaze inward. One may be pleasantly surprised at how easy it is to *feel* and *embrace* the *vibration* of this space. It is ALIVE!!! Here in this benevolent space is where we come to recognize ourselves as *inseparable* aspects of this living breathing *Universe*. We are *consciousness* becoming conscious of itself. This is *Love* in the truest sense!

Realizing this *viscerally*, it becomes easy to remain in the space as the space itself. In a sense we have finally returned home and can feel *God's* embrace. It may be helpful to draw an analogy here. If we were hoping to fall asleep but had a lot on our mind, then falling asleep could prove to be difficult. Attempting to shut down our thinking will rarely prove successful and only add to the restlessness. If instead we relaxed the body allowing the head to fall heavily into the pillow first ...and then focused on the pleasure that deep sleep holds ... and continued to allow the rest of our bodies to fall-fall-fall...deep and deeper into that space of sleep....the thinking would simply be left behind and would eventually evaporate, just as our dreams are left behind upon waking. The beauty of the restful state becomes the Golden Fleece!

The movement is the same in *meditation* when we lead with the heart toward the music of *silence*. By concentrating gently on the heart chakra, simply breathing into it, we can *feel* a deep sense of *peace*, as it is *eternity* itself that is communicated in the space. To feel the beauty and majesty through *conscious reconnection* is a gift—to hear the hum of the *Universe* and to be sweetened by its breath. There is only *Infinite Totality* with no separation of past or future. Once this is understood and we become conscious of this through *feeling/attention* it is very easy to fall in love with our *meditation* practice. It becomes a refuge.

Consider that from inception to birth we were allotted nine months to forge our relationships with our mothers, to fall in love before ever seeing them. *Meditation* is the universal womb. Maintaining a thread of practice is our nine months, figuratively speaking. It is where we cultivate our relationship with the creator that we arise within, fall in love with and return to. Once we turn our gaze inward with *feeling/attention* we will find ourselves longing for another communion with this Divine amalgam of *Spirit, Life Itself* and *Love*.

We enter an eternal field of *redemption* and the womb of creation where there is no longer any consequence for our ignorance, and so the primordial emotion of *guilt* dissipates. No annihilation or destruction occurs in the *Unmanifested Eternity*. Here we can feel our *Immortal Nature*. As we open the heart more and more and feel this deeper reality, it becomes easier to sit in the space for longer periods of time. When the *meditation* session is over, it is imperative that we recognize our state of refreshment and the opportunity to start anew.

This realignment with our *Source* reinstates the homeostasis of the *psycho-physical* body, and so by extension fortifies the *psycho-physical* immune system beyond rational explanation. We discover experientially that there is only *Life*, and only when the death riddle is solved do we begin to live fully.

What About Distractions when Meditating?
A common question I get is: how does one maintain their meditative state when the environment is less than desirable? Perhaps we set out to meditate in a peaceful, quiet park, but not even half-way into the *meditation* people begin to gather. Suddenly there are distractions everywhere -- folks talking, car doors opening and closing, dogs barking, children playing and, yes, screaming. I think you get the idea. This has the potential to end our *meditation* practice, but I say this is a great opportunity to use the environment to go deeply into the *present moment*.

The cacophony of sounds we hear, the differentiating decibel levels and the order in which we hear them will NEVER take place in this way again. This symphony now marks the *present moment*. Here we can listen to the silence behind the sounds, hearing each sound arise, blend and fall away. It is beautiful! Perhaps we can bring the reflection of this moment into even greater relief by listening even more attentively. Perhaps we can hear the flag flapping in the breeze. In fact, we can factor in sensations as well. Never again will we feel a breeze gently caress our face while the sun warms it, as a car engine turns on and a baby cries in that same order and intensity -- never ever again!!! This is what I'm referring to when I suggest a humorous approach. We may have planned on a particular meditation experience, but must remain flexible and adapt. Welcome the moment as it is... *all inclusive.*

Should I be concerned about posture? I've seen pictures of meditators sitting in a lotus position with their feet crossed?

The short answer is yes and no. Now you may think I'm avoiding your question, but I am not. I did not include any instructions concerning posture at the top of the chapter because although posture is a wonderful adjunct to *meditation* it is NOT necessary. The ability to meditate anywhere, anytime and under any conditions should be the goal. We should be capable of falling behind the world of form from wherever and whatever state we are presently in.

Having stated this plainly does not imply that there is no value in attention to posture. A common complaint of many beginners is that they fall asleep during *meditation*. Because through *meditation* we slow down the *mind* the body will oftentimes reflect this as well. As the blood pressure and anxiety levels naturally lower it is sometimes prudent to hold ourselves upright through adherence to posture. In this way we can remain fully attentive and deeply relaxed while not collapsing in on ourselves.

A second and very important reason for adherence to posture may be to appreciate and circulate the energy in the body. When the *mind* is reconnecting with its SOURCE the energy of the body is enhanced, and so proper alignment allows an easy flow of electromagnetic signals from the brain through the brain stem and down the spine. By remaining aligned our energy systems and electromagnetic systems will work in tandem. Although the lotus posture of sitting upright with the legs crossed has become iconic and synonymous with *meditation*, it is not the only acceptable posture. I prefer the taoist sitting posture as it is easier to use by the vast majority of folks. It will require that we use neutral spine posture. If you have forgotten the principles of neutral spine posture refer to the chapter on conscious breathing.

Sit at the end of a straight-back chair so only the sitting bones are making contact with the edge of the seat—for men, the testicles will not be touching the seat. The legs are bent at a right angle so that the thighs are parallel to the ground while the knees to the feet are perpendicular to the ground. It is best to be barefoot. We start by bringing our attention to the soles of our feet. We gently hold our attention at the point where the pad of the big toe and the pad of the little toes separate. It resembles the shape of a Y, and is known as the K1 point in Chinese medicine or reflexology. We can use any kind of prop, such as a penny or wood chip, placed under our K1 point to facilitate sensation. It is useful to know that we draw energy from the earth through this point. Sit upright with the shoulders gently pulled down and back while gently pulling the navel in. The chin is retracted toward the back of the neck, which allows the neck to elongate, taking pressure off the first vertebra. The head should feel as though it is suspended from above by a string. Here it is useful to know that we draw energy from the heavens through the crown chakra located at the top of the head in the center. Our posture should be so aligned that a book could remain atop the head without falling off.

When meditating, it is important that we close down the portals where energy escapes the body, namely the mouth, palms of the hands and soles of the feet. We close off the circuitry in the body so that our chi (internal energy) does not escape and so can be fortified. To close the mouth portal keep the mouth gently closed and the tongue at the roof of the mouth against the palate. A more advanced version is curling the tongue backward toward the heavenly pool behind the front palate. There are two choices concerning closing the portals in the palms of the hands. We can either cup one hand over the other on our laps as if we're holding a butterfly (men right hand on top / women left hand on top), or we can gently connect the thumb and index or middle finger on each hand, and allow our wrists to rest on our thighs, palms facing upward.

Gary Gli

AFFIRMATIONS

"The first step to becoming is to will it."

-Mother Teresa

*A*ffirmations are one of my favorite and most used tools. They are short powerful phrases that are skillfully written and designed to address the specific sticking points that arise within a particular scenario in a given moment. They are carefully worded so as to include and highlight the affirmative resolve against negative thoughts and the associated habit patterns that disempower us. This can include anything and everything from breaking a nicotine addiction to moving on after suffering the loss of a loved one. They may explicitly or implicitly remind us of our *inseparability* from the true *Source* of our *Power* in order that we may prevail and move forward while remaining *whole*.

When circumstances are such that nothing can be done at the moment, an *affirmation* can gently guide us toward *stillness* in order to gather ourselves, or in other instances guide us toward *radical acceptance*. Sometimes they may be constructed in a way that all or several of the aforementioned reminders are included. The true power of the *affirmation* is that it is always written in the light of TRUTH as defined by *Spiritual Science*. No matter how clever we believe ourselves to be, or how positive the inference we come up with, it can never be more powerful than the TRUTH! Moreover, there will never be an instance in our lives where an accepted message of TRUTH will not be the ultimate solution.

More often than not our desire to succeed, whether it be in performance, business, relationships or health, is thwarted by our unconscious *fear-driven impulses, proclivities, tendencies* and *compulsions*. Precisely because they are unconscious, they are expressions of the ego. They run antithetical to our desires and highest aspirations of *redeeming* our *unlimited power*. Remember, *reclaiming* our *power* is inextricably linked to the coveted state of PEACE. These unconscious expressions continue to sabotage us, yet go unnoticed because they are intricately interwoven into the fabric of our personalities. We in turn accept them as givens, and so remain unaware that they hold any sway over us. The interesting thing is that the ego depends on being covert so that it can continue to thrive.

In any scenario where we find ourselves unable to get past *self-doubt* or *powerlessness*, we need to stop and examine what is behind it. An important clue here is that at the root of our dysfunction in any given scenario we will always find *fear, guilt* or *doubt* in one form or another. These three expressions are at the crux of our departure from LOVE and so defile the TRUTH of *inseparability*. They reveal our delusion of being disconnected from our *Source*. *Fear, guilt* and *doubt* will branch out into various other expressions like *angst, anger, frustration, complacency* and/or *indifference*. We may now find ourselves unmotivated and defeated.

As you can see, the further removed from the impetus of our ignorance, the more convoluted the landscape becomes. For example, when *fear* gives way to *anger* and then *indifference*, we become overwhelmed. Because of our self-imposed limited perception we may believe the issue of *indifference* stands alone and/or apart from a deeper snag, and therefore have trouble resolving it. Remember, the ego is clever, and so will find ways to justify our *indifference*. By walking it back and returning to the initial departure from LOVE, which is *fear*, we can more readily find resolve. The ego cannot defend *fear* outright because if it admitted such it would deflate itself. It is in the interest of the ego then to muddy the waters. The ego knows that the more *clarity* we have, the more likely we will be to see it as merely an imposter.

Upon a preliminary investigation we may have trouble connecting the dots or retracing our steps. This is why the clue I gave you earlier is important. It is imperative that we examine the particular issue and parse it as objectively as possible using discernment. The most important question one can ask is: what is separating me from my understanding of the TRUTH? The *Truth* that I am always connected to my *Power*.

Once we expose the ego through contemplative inquiry, it begins to scream because it is threatened. It will fill every corner of our silence but in spite of such, the *inner voice* of our *higher self* is simultaneously and continually whispering. If we remain *vigilant* in turning our gaze inward, guided by the *heart*, which is the seat of our intuition, we can hear that faint voice -- that voice being the voice of the very *Infinite Intelligence* we are forever a part of. What it tells us will prove to be the antidote to the doubt the ego is attempting to sow in each of us, that is, the *doubt* that we have any real *power* at all. In this particular time of COVID-19, doubt may take shape in the downplaying of our *psycho-physical* immune system's power to repel all illness and heal ourselves completely.

I am a big fan of writing my own *affirmations*. The *affirmation* itself is the crystallized resolve or byproduct of a contemplative session. Because we are combining both a creative process and a contemplative practice, the *affirmation* will uphold the power of both, producing a powerful gem.

Throughout my life the writing of *affirmations* has been an important part of my journaling. I have written *affirmations* that I have used for 40 years, others that I have used for four months, some that I used for four days and some that I simply wrote and never used. What is important to know is that this process is always cathartic. There is a healing quality solely in the creation of an *affirmation* regardless of how long we use it or whether or not we use it at all. The *affirmations* that merit keeping, however, will take on a life of their own. Oftentimes they are so broad in their scope they can be used to address several life situations. With each and every use they become emboldened. We are actually building equity in that particular *affirmation* similar in effect to compounded interest. These keepers are extremely powerful and over time provide the intended effect immediately. They eventually become so powerful and alive that we can sometimes feel a shift occur upon uttering the first few lines.

Each scenario or life situation that we find ourselves stuck within will appear like a scene within a movie. We will always be the protagonist and the ego in the form of our *fears* or other negative emotions will be the antagonist. We are in essence rewriting the script directing the protagonist to prevail within the scene. Once the script is written and we are assured to prevail, then we simply play the role. Again, there will be different scenes throughout our lives, and so our *affirmations* will be created accordingly.

Since it is our movie and we get to shape the character of the hero, it is best that WE rewrite the script. However, just as writing scripts is an acquired skill and can be a bit tricky, the same is true for writing *affirmations*. It is perfectly OK, therefore, to use already written *affirmations*. In the same way that an actor who did not write the movie will play the role of the protagonist best by taking direction from the director, your understanding and ability to relate to the provided *affirmations* will enable you to do the same. I will provide a few *affirmations* and break them down in the hopes that they will serve you well as they are written, as well as a template you can refer to when you attempt to create your own. Before I do, however, I will take a moment to share the basic criteria that enables one to write powerful *affirmations*.

The prose of the *affirmation* must be able to conjure up the most comprehensive visual with the fewest number of words. Depending on the intensity of the message we may choose to sprinkle some humor in the appropriate places. As my boxing coach Phil Nastel used to say quite often, "If you can laugh about it, it can't be too bad." Humor can also serve to keep the *affirmation* fresh by breaking the monotony, allowing us to recommit on the next go-round. The cadence can also be sharper at times or more smooth depending on the intention and application of the *affirmation*. Tough-love *affirmations* will have more of a staccato feel, with a short and direct cadence, whereas more ethereal ideas might have more of a legato feel which is a little smoother around the edges.

Rhyming is also important because it is pleasing to the senses, like a nursery rhyme. It can also make the *affirmation* easier to remember. When the prose is written rhythmically against four beats to the measure it can then easily be married to the breath and movement. When this is succinctly done, the *affirmation* takes on an auto-hypnotic cadence which burrows its way deep into the psyche. It is akin to installing a new software program. Think of one of the tools used by the United States Marine Corps to turn young men and women into Marines. They may go into the corps as broken people, but should they survive Boot Camp they will be marines until the day they die. When they're marching they may sometimes sing something like this:

"I don't care what I've been told ...
Can't get hungry, won't get cold…"

And they never do! They get woken up in the middle of the night, hike and run 20 miles, then stand in ice cold water with their rifles over their heads. They have downloaded a software program that tells them their *mind* overrides matter. In truth all there is is MIND. And that *mind* projects itself onto the screen of the senses.

When we change the mind we change the body. As I mentioned earlier, the body becomes malleable, and so healing is possible. Again developing and creating *affirmations* is a bit comprehensive, and so I will provide one for you that can be used specifically at this time dealing with COVID-19. First I will provide the *affirmation*, and then I will break it down so you get the inner meaning:

"My purpose before my pain.
My higher self must reign.
My matrix will sustain.
My matrix will sustain."

I created this *affirmation* for myself when I was dealing with an auto immune dysfunction. Until I healed myself completely I still needed to go to work every day, and my thoughts were consumed by the disease. Knowing full well I had clients who depended on me, I had to ensure that I could shift my mind away from obsessing about my dilemma in order to be available for them.

One of the sure-fire ways for us to *heal* and be made *whole* in times of personal difficulty is to be of *service* to someone else. I thought of this, but also of the fact that I had an aging father who needed me and a woman I was about to marry. This was the purpose of my life at that moment. I had to put that purpose above my pain. Hence the line: "My purpose before my pain." In order to rise above this and to be healed I had to relinquish my whole body being to my *higher self.* Hence the line: "My higher self must reign."

One afternoon I was watching "Super Soul Sunday," with Oprah Winfrey where she was interviewing author and spiritual teacher Mark Nepo. He had dealt with several bouts of cancer, and when Oprah asked him how he managed to go on being so broken, his response was, and I am paraphrasing, "No... parts of me were broken but the whole of me was intact." I thought that was absolutely a brilliant perspective. The lesser parts of ourselves must always be propped up by the greater parts of ourselves. Hence the line: "My matrix will sustain." Now if we apply this prose to the four beats per measure the fourth beat will be silent. It would look like this:

1	2	3	4
My purpose	before	my pain	-
My higher	self	must reign	-
My matrix	will	sustain	-
My matrix	will	sustain	-

This *affirmation* when fully realized should serve you well in dealing with not only COVID-19 but any health crisis. Going forward and in dealing with a variety of other egoic entanglements, perhaps this example along with a few others I will provide will serve as a template to creating your own.

When we marry an *intention* and a *visual* to this *affirmation* it increases its efficacy. Ask yourself what your purpose is now. I'm sure some of you are mothers, sisters, daughters, sons, fathers, doctors, lawyers, sanitation workers, teachers, firemen or small business owners. Regardless of what you do you have a purpose. There are people who love you, need you and depend upon you in ways you may not even realize. When any of us surrender to our *higher angels* we allow *Infinite Intelligence* to flow through us into the world. That *Infinite Intelligence* heals us and all that it touches through us. When you understand this the critical mass of your body being matrix will override any inconsistencies. Using this *affirmation* in this time of COVID-19 and seeing yourself as healed and strong is the mindset necessary to allow your body to wear its *IRON SHIRT*.

Bruce Lipton was a pioneer in the field of epigenetics before that field was fully established, and his experiments proved that our *thoughts* and *beliefs* have the power to turn genes on or off. You may have heard the phrase, "If practice makes perfect, what does perfect practice make?" Well, if this resonates with us at all, it's a short leap to understand that if positive *thoughts* and *beliefs* alter our biology for the better, then surrendering our thinking to the TRUTH will prove to be miraculous.

Here are 2 more affirmations ready to go:

Affirmation #1:

1	2	3	4
In my	heart I	feel God's	song
Always	healthy	young and	strong

Affirmation #2:

1	2	3	4
No such	thing as	sickness	-
No such	thing as	fear	-
Love is	all there	ever	is
My power's	always	here	-

MY PERSONAL STORY DISCOVERING AFFIRMATIONS

I first came to experience the power of *affirmations* in my early 20's. I was training at a boxing gym down in New York City's Soho district. I remember I was sparring with a pretty tough opponent, and I was doing rather well. I was working on a very specific technique, a three point combination, which is a left jab, right cross, left hook. It was really coming together, but occasionally at the end of the exchanges I was getting hit. Although I was getting the better of my opponent, I was not happy about the fact that I did not see some of those punches coming at the end of the exchanges. As I contemplated this on the way home I realized that I was making a mental error. When I succeeded in delivering the technique I stopped for a split second to praise myself, and that's when I would get hit. Other times when my timing was a bit off I stopped to criticize myself, and again I would get hit. I was incredibly bothered by this, but somehow realized that this mental lapse was due to an unconscious tendency. I promised myself I would never forget this lesson and never allow this lapse in my concentration again. I intuitively decided to write my first *affirmation* to ingrain the proper mindset, although at the time I did not realize that that's what it was called. It just seemed like a good idea to auto-suggest — kind of like self-hypnosis. I always had a flair for writing, especially poetry, and so I decided to put something together that I would say to myself to change this mental habit. The following was my first *affirmation*:

"No surrender No retreat Relentless will Focus
No surrender No retreat Relentless will Relax"

Every morning for the next week while doing my morning run I recited this affirmation to myself. When I ran I would time my breathing with my footsteps. Starting as my left foot came down I would breathe in for four steps and out for four steps. In. 2. 3. 4 Out. 2. 3. 4.

I timed the *affirmation* with the breathing and the steps so it was rhythmical. While doing that I would watch myself throwing that left jab, right cross, left hook combo over and over again in my mind, except this time with the appropriate corrections. At the end of each exchange, whether successful or not, I saw myself fully attentive and unwavering mentally while physically either throwing another jab or moving left or right. I interrupted my habit pattern.

The phrase "No surrender No retreat" addressed my focus and unwavering attention. When I said "relentless will" I saw myself imposing my will without breaking my concentration or intention, like a pit bull tugging on a towel, and I reminded myself to stay "focused and relaxed" at the same time. I always believed that those two attributes perfectly balanced and working in tandem were the attributes of a champion. A week later sparring with the same opponent, it was like night and day. This proved to me how successful I could be in such a short period of time by simply changing my thought construct. Interestingly enough, perhaps 15 years later while on stage, I was having a similar problem with lapse in mindset while performing guitar solos. I would invariably make a mistake, then stop to criticize myself, or gloat over a passage that seemed quite good. Mind you, these things happen in a millisecond. I applied the same *affirmation* except this time watching myself play through the mistake or not affording myself the privilege of being my own audience in terms of appreciation. I concentrated instead on the flow and COMPLETION of the idea. Similarly I applied the *affirmation* over one week of morning runs, and I'll never forget that moment on stage when one of the singers turned to me after my solo and said: "been practicing much?"

Gary Gli

VISUALIZATIONS, IMAGINATION and FEELING/ ATTENTION

"Whatever you create in your life you must first create in your imagination." – Tycho Photiou

*V*isualizing is actually quite natural and easy to do. Before we can effectively use this practice, however, we must reclaim our *imagination*. As children we imagine quite readily until we hear those four debilitating words "it's just your *imagination*." Have you ever wondered why *imagination* would be downplayed in such a way? This egocentric world has a vested interest in minimizing the gift of our *imagination*. We are all familiar with the phrase "misery needs company," and what is misery but limitation?

Our *imagination* rests at the seat of *creation*, which holds the promise of *limitless expansion* and *liberation*. Therefore, any engagement in *creation* is antithetical to the desires of the ego, because *creation* in the truest sense is a surrender to the *Infinite*, where the ego holds no sway. The ego DEPENDS on our investment in the finite to sustain its existence. If we understand this, then it becomes evident why the world, or collective ego, would unconsciously undermine *imagination*. Regardless of how it has been undermined we use *imagination* more than we realize. Can you think of anything at all in the man-made universe — a car, a plane, a bench, a hammer, a television set, or anything else — that did not arise in man's *imagination* first and foremost? An inventor invents something that is needed by first *visualizing* that object in his mind before it can be made. Athletes and performing artists witness their successful performances in their heads long before the events occur. We all plan engagements, weddings, bar mitzvahs, graduation parties and other events in our minds as preparation. So, as you can see, we all use *imagination* but unfortunately place restrictions upon it. This speaks to our perceived limitations, not the limitation of *imagination*. All children have imaginary playmates. Do we?

Until we grant ourselves permission to imagine FREELY once again we will remain incapable of using this gift of *visualization* profoundly and effectively. Through *visualization* we are able to transform the world of matter, because, although matter APPEARS to be *real*, it is not. Only that which is *Real* holds the power to change that which is not. As proof that the world of form is illusory, consider the fact that all that integrates in this world... disintegrates. Clouds, microbes, insects, fish, animals, planets, stars, people......pretty much everything but Keith Richards. NOTHING in the temporal plane prevails, and so has no reality of its own. Space, which, once again, is comprised of

Spirit, Infinite Intelligence and *Life Itself,* remains immutable. It is REAL precisely because it is *infinite, eternal* and *indestructible.* This is a very important distinction. As has been expressed throughout this work, our *Spirit* is inseparable from the *Infinite Intelligence* that comprises space or the *Unmanifested.* Beyond the body we are eternal beings. The *Spirit* in us "creates," as *creation* in the truest sense is an *extension* of the *Infinite,* while the ego "makes," which is a projection of its desires and needs in the finite.

What does it mean when we say that *creation* is an *extension* of the *Infinite?* Plainly stated, it is an *extension* of *harmony.* Have you ever stared at a painting or listened deeply to a piece of music that arrested your attention, anchoring you to the *eternal present moment?* Could you perhaps feel the timeless beauty expressed there? This is why we create masterpieces but make wrenches. When the intention is something as noble as *Healing,* which in the deepest sense portends being made *Whole,* we can be assured that we are in a process of *"creating,"* not "making." Because of this we can commit to our intention without fear of failure. All *creation* on the temporal plane serves the *purification* of the *Individual Spirit,* therefore, it is lasting and *real* even beyond death.

Okay, I get that in essence Healing goes beyond the body, but what about the body? How exactly do we heal the body? When each *individual mind* reflects *Divine Mind,* even if it is just for a moment while *visualizing,* it channels *Infinite Power.* That *Power* is expressed through our *intention* to *heal* or *create*, and does so through the metaphysical realm. It is useful to remember that the world of form is subservient to the currents in the metaphysical realm, where energy is king. All matter is comprised of energy vibrating at different frequencies. By altering frequency we influence matter. The body is malleable, as has been proven through the field of epigenetics. Neuroplasticity, the brain's ability to undergo structural or physiological changes, is also proven science. When we receive guidance from our *Highest Mind*, and *create* through the metaphysical by altering and transforming energies, the world of form and anything in it follows suit. *Imagination* and *visualization* directly influence the manipulation and alteration of energies in the metaphysical, as does *meditation* and the use of *affirmations*. This is *Divine Alchemy*, and it is our birthright. We were created in the image and likeness of the *Creator*, and so we too must *create*.

Imagination and *visualization* at first require an *extension* of *faith*. Through their use and cultivation we learn the TRUTH concerning *creation* and transformation in the world of form on an experiential level. We come to *know* and *trust* unequivocally in our *power* and the *power* of these practices. Another important thing to understand about *imagination* is that it is the precursor to *intuition*, which enables us to download continually all we need to know from the *cosmic internet*. The most important bit of knowledge we download is that all things are possible.

Visualization is the marriage of *imagination* and *feeling/ attention*, especially where healing the body is concerned.

Feeling/attention requires nothing more than applying our sensibility to feel energetic resonance in the areas of the body that we choose to focus on. We can also feel energy coursing through the whole body being at once if we choose. By simply activating *feeling/attention* married to an *intention* of *healing* we leave the rest up to *Universal* or *Infinite Intelligence.* Just as when we were in the womb and took no part in our *creation*, we must *trust* that this *Intelligence* will know exactly what to do. Remember the *Power* that *created* us is the very same *Power* that *heals* us. When we rise up in the name of *God* doing our part, *God* returns the favor. As the saying goes, "God helps those who help themselves."

All we need do is bring our *attention* to any area of discomfort with an *intention to heal* and hold that space in the *full knowledge* that healing is possible. We may need to be consistent and persistent in our efforts. One last but very important lynchpin is that the most powerful expression of *visualization* is to see that which is intended as if it has ALREADY come to pass.

Here is an exercise and two Visualizations:
It is always important to remember that when we invite ourselves to a *self-actualized mind/body* healing party, we bring *intention* and *attention*, and *Infinite Intelligence* provides everything else. Therefore, it is our job to cultivate *feeling/attention.*

Cultivating *feeling/attention* in the body is not difficult, but can be taken to great depths. These first 2 examples are

69

simple, but the one following these two will take some time and patience before bearing fruit.

Example 1) We'll start by simply closing our eyes and bringing *attention* to our limbs. Let's bring *attention* to our hands and *feel* the *life* within them. Perhaps we can clap them a few times then pause and feel the activity. Simple enough. Yes?

Example 2) Let's lie down, take a few conscious breaths and then remain still for a moment. When we are ready we can bring our *attention* to our feet and relax them. Feel them falling into the ground, if you will. After a moment or two we can move up the body, relaxing our shins and calves. We can *feel* the tension rising off of them like steam off of boiling water. We can continue until we relax the entire body. The jaw line and cheeks are areas that we can feel quite easily.

This next exercise is a modification of a more comprehensive Taoist meditation meant to appreciate and circulate internal energy (chi) within the body. This exercise will still yield some of the benefits of the more comprehensive meditation, but we are using it primarily to help us bring *feeling/attention* to life.

Within our subtle body is a flow of energy (chi) on a central highway, if you will, known as the microcosmic orbit or small heavenly cycle. It is comprised of a front and back channel. Beginning at the naval energy center (dantian), energy flows down under the genitalia up the spine around the crown of the head down through the third eye, throat, chest and back to the naval.

This is a crude description, as there are fourteen energy centers in fourteen precise points. If we were to include the legs and feet we could add three more. This subject is too vast to cover here, and there are whole books that go into great depth on the microcosmic orbit and more. I chose a handful of energy centers for this study because I find them to be more highly sensitive than the others. We can easily begin to feel the magic of living activity in these centers when we focus *feeling/attention* on them.

As with the breathing, sit at the end of a chair, knees bent at a right angle, holding ourselves upright in neutral spine posture. Men, be sure to cup your hands on your lap right over left, and women, left over right. Keep the mouth closed with the tongue touching the soft palate behind the front teeth. By bringing *feeling/attention* to the crown of the head (pineal gland) and gently focusing our attention there we can feel it come to life. At first it may be necessary to imagine something like drops of water gently falling one at a time onto the crown of our heads. After holding our inner gaze here for a bit we can then move our *feeling/attention* to the third eye, which is the point between the eyebrows (pituitary gland). Looking deeply within ourselves we will feel a gentle pulse there.

Let us now bring our *feeling/attention* to the perineum which is the point between the testicles and the anus or the vagina and the anus. Feel the inner movement, feel the sensation. Next, we bring our *feeling/attention* to the tailbone (coccyx). Relax it and feel it come to life. Finally, we bring our *feeling/ attention* back to the dantian which is two inches below the navel and sit with it awhile. We let the energy collect here before ending the exercise.

Again, in a complete microcosmic orbit meditation we would begin at the dantian circle downward and around up the spine awakening all fourteen energy centers and end at the dantian where we would circle, gather and blend the chi. As mentioned earlier, although what I shared here is an incomplete microcosmic orbit meditation, we will still garner many of the benefits concerning the organs related to the energy centers explored. My greater intention once again was to help us realize the agency of *feeling/attention*. Be patient, as it will take a while to cultivate this ability. Until we do, this will serve as a wonderful meditative concept to help to *still* the *mind*.

Once we have cultivated this ability we are free to *create* with it. Anytime we feel pain or distress in the body we can simply bring our *feeling/attention* to where the pain is with an *intention to heal*. We may choose to feel heavenly energy enter through the crown of the head, and further direct it to anywhere in the body. Occasionally we can use *visualizations* like light or steam surrounding the pain.

In a traditional *microcosmic orbit meditation conscious breathing* does not apply. However, because we are using this *meditation* to awaken *feeling/attention* first and foremost, we can gently breathe into these energy centers, feeling them expand. We can then use the breath as the vehicle to bring *healing vibration* of any kind to wherever we choose.

This second one is a great *visualization/meditation*. Looking up toward the sun, especially on a sunny day, we can gently close our eyes until all we see is light in every direction. *Imagine* that beautiful soft yellow light gently coming through our lightly closed eyelids. We smile into the sun, then put our noses up toward it like a dog, and breathe the sunlight into our bodies. We must *feel* the warm sunlight entering our nostrils and filling our bodies from our toes up to our heads with warm healing light.

As with all *visualizations* this must be a visceral experience. We are completely filled with light. Now we hold the breath and the light in our bodies — we relax our skin. We *feel* the light outside the body gently merging and connecting with the light inside our bodies. Our physical bodies disappear and our *consciousness* is floating in a sea of light. There is nothing but the light. We are the light. The shadow behind us has disappeared. Now we exhale into the light, and breathe it back into our bodies again.

Remember... we are existing in a world of nothing but light. KNOW that this light is the most healing entity on the planet. The sun is in every cell of our bodies. We are pure light, and must KNOW we are healed by the light!

Many years ago I heard the story of how Native American tribes would stand in the fields and breathe in the first storm of each new season. Before the rain came they would breathe in the power and energy of the storm winds, the thunder and the lightening. In this way they became one with the new season. Their immune systems recalibrated and harmonized with the new season, and so were fortified against the pathogens, viruses and bacteria that the season would bring. More than that, however, it was a way of unifying with the storm and mother earth.

I often go into a field or park on stormy days and nights, face the oncoming winds and breathe their energy into my body. As the trees move and sway in the wind, I breathe in their life and majesty. I am empowered and strengthened as I become one with the scene before me.

PURPOSE AND ADVERSITY

"Take the first step in faith. You don't have to see the whole staircase, just take the first step." - Martin Luther King, Jr.

As Eckhart Tolle brings to light in his book "The Power of Now," each individual on the planet has two purposes, an outer purpose and an inner purpose. Our outer purposes will vary. We can be a teacher, fireman, business owner, sanitation worker and on and on. Our inner purpose, on the other hand, is the same for all of us. It is to discover our *Authentic Nature,* which is *inseparable* from the *Source* of all *Intelligence* and *Power.*

Whether we choose to take up this calling or not in any given life segment is up to us. I assure you that eventually in this life or another you will be inclined to do so, as our spiritual destiny to fulfill this inner purpose will never relent. At some point we may be motivated to fulfill this curriculum through a crisis or some other form of suffering. This time of COVID-19 may be that opportunity for any one of us.

The COVID-19 crisis is merely a snapshot of what is occurring at this particular moment in time. What is ubiquitous, however, is *adversity*. We can count on the fact that there will always be *adversity* in one form or another. It is inherent in the world of form. Therefore, this particular snapshot in time affords us an opportunity to rise to the occasion with a sense of *spiritual purpose* and *grace*.

For me as a spiritual teacher, this crisis provided me the opportunity, not only to help you navigate this difficult time, but also perhaps to *awaken* in you this calling to fulfill your own inner purpose now and moving forward. If you are a novice in terms of using these tools and practices to raise your *consciousness*, perhaps this stoked your interest. If you are someone who is already experienced and using these practices, perhaps it brought them into greater relief or helped smooth out some rough edges.

Keep in mind that oftentimes rising to the occasion will begin by offering no resistance to what is already the case. After all, what is, is. One would be surprised by just how much *strength* and *courage* is needed to simply *accept* the conditions the *present moment* may reveal. By retreating into the *stillness*, we expand our perception, and so discover inherent qualities we may not have known we had. Once we have gathered ourselves we are ready to seize the moment and move past *fear, guilt* and *doubt*, returning once again to *Love*.

In doing so, we must remember not to judge ourselves too

harshly. We must remember that we are reaching for an ideal in the hopes of moving ourselves closer to it, though we may never fully embody it here on earth. In simply forging a relationship with our *higher selves,* we breathe a sigh of relief in the revelation that we are ALREADY *redeemed.* Knowing this alleviates much of the self-imposed pressure of *guilt* and *doubt* while emboldening our *courage, self-forgiveness* and *faith.* We realize we are never truly alone in fulfilling our *Divine Purpose* -- the purpose of discovering and teaching TRUTH by example, which, in effect, is an act of *Healing* both ourselves and the world at large.

Gary Gli

SAMPLE OF COMBINED PRACTICES

Here is an example of purposefully combining several tools in order to create a powerful protocol for supercharging the immune system. I would recommend starting and ending the day with this protocol. Try this for 21 days and see how you feel.

Start off by either sitting or lying in neutral spine posture. If you're lying down you can place a pillow or foam roller under your knees so that the back relaxes. Close your eyes, smile and take a nice, deep, full breath. Continue smiling while feeling your body fully expanded. Enjoy the oxygenation of your blood. Hold your breath for as long as you can. Do not struggle with it, just allow the pressure to gently build so that when you exhale it would be as though you let the air out of a balloon to buzz around the room. Now let go of the breath and feel all the tension rush from your body tickling your lips on the way out. As the air rushes from your body it should sound like a sigh.

Now let's start with some simple belly breathing. You will breathe in for four counts and out for four counts. This is considered one cycle. Gently *feel* the belly rise and *feel* the belly fall. Smile as you do this exercise for three cycles. Now take another deep breath high up in the chest while you *smile.* Hold it again for as long as you can and as the air rushes out of your body the second time *feel* yourself falling into a deeper state of relaxation.

Now let's spend some time watching your thoughts while putting a period at the end of each thought that arises. Gently sit in the space between the thoughts. Do not wrestle with your thinking. If a second thought arises let it come and then put a period at the end of that thought as you would a sentence. As you sit in the spaces *feel* your state of *awareness. Feel* the *life* in the *present moment.* Hold this but for a short while. Now take another deep breath expanding the body while smiling. Hold it again for as long as you can and this time when you let go of the breath you will *feel* yourself slipping into an even deeper state of relaxation.

Now you will say the following short affirmation: *I and the universe are one. The universe and I are one. I and the universe are one.* Take a moment here to let go of your thoughts and concept of self, and *feel yourself merging with totality.* In this pause hold the *knowing* that your health is reinstated and your immune system will absolutely protect you against all invaders and pathogens. *Know* that you cannot be sick.

Now let's do the tailbone breathing. You're breathing gently into the lower back for four counts and then out for eight counts and holding your lungs empty for four counts before beginning again. Remember the first breath of the next inhalation cycle must be 25%. Do this for three rounds.

Now bring your *attention* to your navel, and *imagine* a golden cord from your navel extending outward deep, deep, deep into the universe. This is an umbilical cord and you are connected to the *Infinite*. You are a child of God. *Feel* the *healing* energy entering your body. *Feel* the *grace* afforded you by this *Infinite Intelligence* that you are *forever* a part of.

Now begin breathing into either the belly or the lower back for four counts and out for four. Apply the *affirmation*: *In my heart I feel God's song... always healthy young and strong.* Remember to keep it four beats to the measure. Be sure to synchronize it with your breath and *smile*. Ponder the words as you say them. Remember this physical plane is malleable and our *intentions* and *affirmations* shape our *reality*.

Again, try this first thing in the morning and before bed for 21 days. Of course be mindful of your consumption and use the supplements I suggested. Remember, you are fortifying your *IRON SHIRT* by your commitment and adherence to this simple protocol, and so will be protected. *Amen.* When we say *"Amen"* we crystallize our intention because *"Amen"* can be translated to mean: "and it is so."

Gary Gli

You can never say it all.

The ears and the years that surround you are often

too short,

And the mouth is far too long.

No, you can never say it all.

You can only hope to say enough and stand for it all.

\- Gary Gli

Gary Gli

Gary Gli

Ironshirtprotocol@hotmail.com
www.facebook/garygliconsciousmovement.com
www.linkedin.com/in/GaryGli

Gary Gli

Gary Gli

Gary Gli

Made in the USA
Middletown, DE
06 August 2020